THE OTHER SIDE

HOW PROVERBS CHALLENGE THE WORLD AS WE KNOW IT

Story & Essays by Michael J. Thate

Concept & Curation by Lukas V. Naugle

Book design by Nathan Black Design,
www.nathanblackdesign.com

ISBN 978-0-9909870-0-0

Published by
The One Institute
1 North 1st Street, Suite 700
Phoenix, AZ 85004

For Brian MacKay

whose crayon colors outside the lines with wit and wisdom.

CONTENTS

CHOKING ON TRUTH

"The world is filled with too much truth."

This was the claim of the Austrian psychoanalyst, Otto Rank—one of Freud's closest colleagues who would later be among his sharpest critics. Ernest Becker reflected upon this aphorism in his Pulitzer Prize winning book, *The Denial of Death.*

> The [person] of knowledge in our time is bowed down under a burden [they] never imagined [they] would ever have: the overproduction of truth that cannot be consumed. For centuries [humanity] lived in the belief that truth was slim and elusive and that once [they] found it the troubles of [humanity] would be over. And here we are in the closing decades of the 20th century, choking on truth [...] The mind is silent as the world spins on its age-old demonic career.[1]

In a slightly different way, Nassim Taleb reflected upon this phenomenon in his little book, *The Bed of Procrustes*. Taleb laments,

> We humans, facing limits of knowledge, and things we do not observe, the unseen and the unknown, resolve the tension by squeezing life and the world into crisp commoditized ideas, reductive categories, specific vocabularies, and prepackaged narratives, which, on the occasion, has explosive consequences.[2]

Despite our best efforts at squeezing its complexities into "crisp commoditized ideas," the world is forever and always expanding beyond the lightning chase of our categorization and hubris.

This little book follows Rank, Becker, and Taleb in challenging these "prepackaged narratives" through a re-staging of the book of Proverbs—that collection of aphorisms which sprung from the Levantine soul. To be clear, this is not the standard commentary. It is a kind of illumination of its collected aphorisms. Illuminated manuscripts are manuscripts where visual markers are added to the text—these markers are called marginalia—in order to enhance and play at meanings latent within (and outside) the text.

All of us fall into the ruts of forming mental patterns to the neglect of what may rest outside those well-worn trails of thought. We cease reading and listening to the familiar because we think we know what it says. The beauty of Proverbs and the Wisdom tradition is that the aphorisms collected challenge the truths we set upon them by refusing to be tidied or made familiar or timeless. Like the aphorisms of the ancient Skeptics, of Nietzsche, of Confucius and Wittgenstein, of Wilde and Papeš, and of Marie von Ebner-Eschenbach, the aphorisms of Proverbs shock, unsettle, and force us to consider wisdom as a narrative world that troubles the stability of our own. The aphorist is the great iconoclast. She does not name or define so much as she unmasks and destabilizes.

Through story, essay, and visualization, this little book is an attempt at illumination, at conjuring the subversive power of wisdom within the book of Proverbs through the perspectives of love, horror, and epic. Each genre reveals a distinct shade to the many-sided nature of wisdom: her expanse, her entreaties, her latent danger. By approaching wisdom from the perspective of these familiar genres of love, horror, and epic, we attempt to make Proverbs strange once more so we might see and hear these collected aphorisms afresh. It is an attempt to punch a world that is choking on truth in the stomach so that the fresh air of wisdom might return. This punchy little book attempts to leave the clear borders of this and that, of right and wrong, and dare its readers to walk the way of the other side: the way of wisdom.

THE TRAVELER:

AN EPIC MYTH OF HORROR AND LOVE

Where now? Who now? When now?

> —SAMUEL BECKETT, THE UNNAMABLE (1953)

What we call the beginning is often the end. And to make an end is to make a beginning.

> —T.S. ELIOT, LITTLE GIDDING (1942)

There once was a young man who was held prisoner. The land had been caught within the throes of a long war. Everywhere was confusion and fear. The war seemed to erase memory. And people traversed from one side to the other. There was no history here.

This was a very strange prison. There was some cruel magic that floated throughout the camp, like a mist, unsettling the mind and causing prisoners to see phantoms. They never knew if what was before them was real. Some were driven mad. But everything felt real. A prisoner could be receiving a beating from the prison guards only to see them vanish before their eyes; or eating gruel in the mess hall only to see it turn into a lavish feast and then into maggots. The barbed wire, the guns, and the walls—everywhere walls—seemed to change as well. Sometimes it seemed that there was nothing there. One of the prisoners, a wiry old man with sullen eyes, wandered off one day because he said it was all a dream.

"We must all walk toward the light," he said, walking toward the morning sun.

He was promptly shot down and devoured by the guard dogs—those foul hellhounds.

The young man was wedged into the same bunks with about a dozen others. Though he couldn't remember exactly when, another young man appeared. Most of the prisoners kept to themselves. But prisons create odd alliances. And fate cast its die, placing these two together.

Now these two young men were both cunning in their

own fashion. And together the two discovered a way out
of the prison. When the guards changed shifts for the last
time before first light of each day, they appeared to be
at their weakest. The one had dreamed—or, at least he
thought he had—that the supply shack near the southwest
corner of the camp had a couple of damaged tiles. When
he awoke he brought the other and they discovered it to
be the case. The shack stood about 10 meters from the
shape-shifting fence. Sometimes the fence appeared 15
meters high; sometimes it didn't appear to be there at all.
The two young men had devised a plan to sneak into the
shack during the final watch and tunnel underneath the
fence on the other side. After many nights of tunneling
they were ready to escape. The night had come. The one
decided to let the other bunkmates in on their plan. But it
became clear that some simply enjoyed having something to
talk about, something to debate, something with which to
distract themselves. Even the other started to wane after a
while. At first, the other suggested patience. Not long after
he began pointing out how the prison wasn't that bad. The
one reasoned with the other each night, however, and the
other finally relented. They decided to escape the following

night and the one set out the final plans to the group.

Now that the night was set for escape, only these two young men ventured out. Some complained of fatigue and illness, others that the timing wasn't right, and still others about the hellhounds outside.

"We can't go," they said, "It wouldn't be safe. And who's to say what is on the other side of the fence?"

The one tried to convince the others to risk the escape.

Terrible dreams began to haunt the one. But just as he woke the memory of the dreams was scared off as if by some animal's snarl. He could hear indiscernible whispers every now and then, and a panic set over him. As the days carried on, the nightmares grew worse. Each night he would be startled awake by a flash of light and a shout.

"Traveler!" it would hiss.

The final night the one awoke the other with a scream. This time he had seen a face—a face so foul and frightening yet immediately forgotten once awoken. The other tried to calm him.

"We can't stay here," he said with terror, refusing the other's comfort. "We will die. That is certain."

The two talked long into the night and realized that their only chance for survival and escape was to leave without the others. The rest would never be ready. To risk, to gamble, to venture out into the unknown was their only chance. The two decided it wouldn't be safe to leave the barracks until the rest were asleep.

"Perhaps they would keep us from leaving? Or, worse: inform on us!" the one said to the other.

So they pretended to sleep until they heard the sleeping sounds of the others and then stole into the night toward the shack. They lifted the tiles that covered their secret, dove into the cramped tunnel, and burrowed like little moles. Finally they had come to the other side. They peaked their heads out to see if it was clear. The camp looked different from the other side. All they saw were walking corpses. Around the perimeter there was a green translucent mist that seemed to envelop the camp.

"Where's the wall?" asked the other.

The one didn't respond.

As they looked into the mist they couldn't help but feel an odd sensation: a kind of cocktail of relief and anxiety. What do we do now on the other side of this place? But the sight of the phantom corpses quickened their resolve to leave. They both whispered to each other that they were escaping a graveyard as they filled in the tunnel, and then sped off into the night as quickly as their malnourished legs would allow.

There was no cover; no forest into which to escape. Their only chance was to race outside the reach from the eyesight of the guards before the morning sun laid bare the destitute land. For hours they ran. It was as if their bodies, sensing freedom, remembered their abilities that night. On and on they ran, deeper and deeper into the night, until they began to see the first glimpses of the sun. It was an odd sight. Was this their first sunrise of freedom or the spotlight that would betray their escape? They ran on tiptoe and with their breath held tightly lest they would somehow alarm unsuspecting watchers. On an on they ran like this. Their pace slowed as they began to feel overcome with thirst and fatigue. The other collapsed to the ground, while the one urged him on.

"Not yet! We can't stop!"

"Let me be just for a moment… Just a moment…" panted the other.

The one grabbed the other by the shoulder. "We can't stop. We're too close. We must keep moving until we're completely out of sight."

They felt some comfort in that the camp was a speck in the distance by now. The one encouraged the other to get up and move until they could no longer see the camp. The other cussed and begrudgingly agreed.

After another few days they decided to slow their pace. Every now and then they thought they heard the faint bark of the hellhounds, but they didn't feel under threat of the guards. Had they ever given chase? There was also some cover now. The land was a vast wilderness, but there were crags and boulders strewn throughout that the two weaved in between. It had been several days since they had eaten anything so they decided their priorities had to shift from escape to survival.

"We are free," the other would say. "Now we must eat!"

The one relented. He knew the other was right. Just then the other heard something moving in the distance.

"What's that?"

"What's what?"

A subtle snap rang out in the distance.

"That!"

The one pressed to listen but he couldn't hear anything. He suddenly grew alarmed.

"We should keep moving," the one whispered.

The two broke their clandestine camp and stole back into the night. On they labored through the wilderness that seemed to expand with their every step. The rocky ground punctured their blistered feet and cut into their knees and hands when they fell.

The next night it happened again.

"Something's following us," said the other. "Something's out there."

The one quickly smothered fire.

"We must move."

"But we've been running for so long," the other protested. "Maybe whoever is out there following us is trying to help."

"Don't be a fool," said the one. "We've stayed too long."

The two finally slumped off. They grubbed on worms and whatever else they could find. Their spirits seemed to grow darker and colder with the passing nights. The other began to grow bitter towards the one and blamed him for their hardships.

"We had it better in the prison," he would say. "At least we had a meal everyday. Out here we only have worms and bugs, and god knows whatever else we can find."

As the other's mood soured, the one felt a mounting weight hung around his neck. The other was right: the prison provided a kind of comfort. Every day fell into predictable patterns. In the prison camp he thought he was starving, but he'd rather have the gruel and slop compared to the filth on which they grubbed in the wilderness. Desperation began to settle into the one's spirit. Something must be done, he thought. But what?

Finally the other slumped down.

"No further. I can't go on," his voice crackled with insolence.

The one felt the weariness too, but knew they should keep moving. He tried to urge the other on. Reluctantly he stooped to start a small fire, nibbling at his fingers until sleep began to overtake him. He sat with his knees curled to his chin, staring into the fire for answers. He shot a drowsy look over to the other and saw him sprawled out asleep. The fire cracked and hissed, lulling the one into a trance. He felt the desperation return. It covered him, like a blanket left out in the rain, sticking to him and weighing him down. He felt a tear forming in his eye but it never fell. His eyes grew even more tired and he felt them close. Wild dreams came to him that night. Phantoms and monsters floated in and out of the shadows of his mind. There was a terror that clouded his sleep—like being thrown into a dungeon. He felt around for the walls but could not find them; he searched for a door but his eyes could not focus in the dark. Though feeling nothing around him, the nothingness suddenly collapsed upon him. Though no walls could be seen or touched, he could feel some foreboding closing in on him. He thought he could hear laughter and whispers. At first it sounded like the hissing of some animal stalking him in the darkness. A form began to materialize, and the hissings became discernable.

"You are not safe here, traveler."

A face sprang from the black into the face of the one. It was covered by pox and worms, with patchy hair crawling with lice. The eyes were fiery red, mismatched and crossed.

"You are not safe here!" it screamed.

Then the light. A grey, pulsating light, illuminating the mockery their freedom had taken. The one shot awake like a sprung trap. He looked over to the other and saw him transfixed. What was he looking at? Everything in him was sore and painful. He grimaced as he shifted his tired body to follow the other's gaze. The pale rising of the sun blinded him. He lifted his hand to shield a line of sight. And there she was.

She came with the morning. Amidst the grey and gloom the rock and ruin, of the wilderness she shone in white. Her lips were of scarlet, her hair a fierce black. Her eyes sparkled green with equal parts welcome and mystery. She stood taller than most women and her fully formed body was hinted at from underneath her white linens. The two men looked at her dumbly. Funny things happen to a man freshly out of prison in the presence of a woman. But this was no ordinary woman. She smelled of fine oils and her bleached linens reflected the sun like some terrible cherub. Were this presence before them the entirety of the prison guards and the pound of the hellhounds, the two would have fought tooth and claw. But before the woman they lay dumbstruck, like some field mouse before a rising adder.

"Come," she said, turning to walk away.

The other rose and followed, but the one reached for his arm.

"No," he pleaded.

The other ripped his arm free.

"You've been leading us nowhere," he snapped with a whisper. "This is the way. You can follow or stay out here and starve."

The other glared at him as he turned to catch up to this lady of wonder. The one sat, watching them walk off. The other was right: he didn't know where he was going. He didn't even know where he was. But should he trust this presence? What else is there guiding them? There was a pulsating allure about her. He must follow this woman! But that dream... that voice. Was it hers? Did she visit him in his dream? Or was it about her? He grabbed a handful of the wilderness dirt and slammed it down in disgust.

"Something isn't right," he cussed under his breath, but nonetheless rose and slumped on to catch up with the other and the mysterious woman.

The grey wilderness was all alit now. Dirty and half-dead, the one and the other followed the woman of spectacular beauty and radiant light like some dumb animal. There was no talking during the journey. The woman walked ahead with her regal stride, never once looking behind. Of course they followed, she must have thought. Who could possibly refuse her? The one and the other followed in a trance like captives.

They soon happened upon what looked like a lavish farm. As they walked up the lane they noticed the animals running up to the fence, squealing. The one looked around and guessed at what appeared to be terror in these animals' eyes. He looked to the woman to ask her about them but was startled by a fierce glare she gave these animals. Her green eyes seemed to burn like a licking flame. As they continued walking he noticed a lush vegetable garden.

Every kind of vegetable was there. The plants swayed rhythmically, but not with the wind. It was like they were writhing either in some ecstasy or agony, or dancing to some unheard chorus. He looked again at the woman and saw her mouthing something to the garden. He dared not ask her anything.

The woman led them into a large room with a pool of steaming water and floating flower petals.

"Give me your clothes," the woman demanded.

The two obeyed, like children would their mother, and disrobed in front of the woman. They covered their embarrassments with their hands and stood naked before her. She gathered their clothes, and told them to wash up.

"Dinner will be served in an hour. Freshen up. You will dine with me tonight."

The two stepped into the pool of water. At first they trembled. They looked at each other as if waiting for a trap to spring, or wishing after some answer. Then the other began to splash in delirium. The one looked around suspiciously. Was this another trick of dark magic? Were they still in the prison camp somehow? He looked around the poolroom and noticed the heads of wild animals hung as trophies. He started to feel lightheaded, lulled into a deep, relaxing daze by the steam of the pool. But all those years in the prison had made him suspicious. He picked up one of the flower petals, testing it to see if it was real.

"We need to be careful," said the one to the other as he twisted the petal between his fingers.

"Careful? We are free!" shouted the other as he fell playfully backward into the pool. He splashed water onto the one. The one looked to the exuberance of the other. His bitterness seemed to be washed away by the pool. The one felt a tremble forming along the side of his face; a strange cracking and stretching of his sun-dried lips. He felt his mouth with his fingers. What was this foreign sensation forming across his face?

When the two had finished their baths, they noticed clean clothes laid out for them, warm clothes with neither holes nor lice. They were clean and warm for the first time they could remember. Their newfound comfort quickened them to the rotting holes in their stomachs. They were famished. And just as their hunger pangs pinged loudest, the aroma of dinner floated into their nostrils.

"Food!" cried the other.

The two raced to the dinning hall where they found an immaculate table set before them. Their every desire seemed to be there: pork, lamb, beef, chicken, goat; lush vegetables from the garden; and flowing red wine. The succulent smells caused an intense watering in their mouths and a shivering through their jaws and down their spine. They looked at the table in wonderment. Both began to weep. In the presence of the table, the one remembered his dread these many years and the anxiety and fatigue of the last weeks. They were safe, he thought. At long last, they were safe.

And then the woman strode in. She had changed her flowing white linens for a tighter fitting satin dress. The dress was a soft violet color, and clung to her body like a lover. She took her seat at the head of the table and gestured for the two to sit.

"Eat," she said.

The other grabbed for the food as if it might disappear and began shoveling it into his mouth—each bite before he could chew the previous one. The one looked around and considered the table before him. He looked at the other who seemed to be becoming animal-like and then to the woman who was smiling crookedly at him.

"Are you not hungry?" she asked the one.

"Yes… I'm…"

"Then eat. Take your fill. You will never find a table like this," she said with a sneer.

The one looked at her and was again overtaken with her beauty. She was leaning back in her chair with one arm elegantly flung over the back of it. Her legs were crossed, with one of her knees protruding from the violet gown, luring the one's sight further upstream her mighty river. The gown hung loosely over her breasts, barely containing its secrets. He followed her neck up to her lips. He was drunk looking at her. He then looked her full in the face. Her emerald green eyes were waiting for him. He was reminded of the green mist around the prison and the room began to swirl. She was saying something to him but he could not see her lips moving. She was growing fierce, and suddenly a flash of light overcame him.

The hissings and whispers returned—and then the voice.

"You are not safe here, traveler!"

The voice roused him from the woman's hypnotic gaze. Where that voice came from was lost upon the one. He looked over to the other who paused momentarily as if he heard something too. The one could no longer keep the sights and sounds straight. The grunts and animal sounds resumed from the other as he ate. A ferocious glee was cast over the face of the woman as she watched him. But that voice—where did it come from? The spinning room overtook him and soon all went dark.

The darkness swirled and stirred the hissings and dancing of the phantoms. Images of a distant land flashed and then disappeared—like a landscape illuminated by a storm and then gone. The land flashed again but this time was aflame. First the fiery green eyes of the woman of spectacular beauty, and then the prison shone covered by the green mist. The lightening cracked the black glass a final time, and the face of the haggard woman shouted out from behind it:

"Traveler!"

The one wasn't certain how long he had been out when he was startled awake. When he finally came to he found himself on a large bed with satin sheets perfumed with oils. He tried to pull himself up, but he collapsed back onto the bed like a rotted tree. Even though he had been sleeping this whole while, he didn't feel refreshed. The dreams played through his mind as he lay sprawled across the bed. He struggled to push himself up against the headboard of the bed, and looked around the room. The room was filled with every luxury. How could such a place exist in this barren wasteland? The one thought back to the way that was lined with thorn and rock. And now this: decadence everywhere.

He stumbled out of the bed and into the hallway. The walls seemed to swirl hypnotically: one moment fantastical images would appear, then they would flash monstrous. One moment serene, the next chaotic. With alternating steps the hallway would shift between a place of wonderment and terror. Suddenly, a wave of panic came over him. He looked in vain for some door that led outside to the farm. Each door he tried opened to a new room of opulence.

"There is no way out," he whispered, as if to the riches spread around him. "We are prisoners."

"Prisoners?" sung a voice, which sounded like the pouring of mulled wine.

The one shot around and saw an open door from which the voice came. He walked slowly toward the open door. The sounds of laughter and a pulsating amber glow spilled out the opening. The one suddenly felt alone, and an overwhelming longing to enter and join the laughter washed over him. He held his breath, and tiptoed toward the opening, peering cautiously into the room.

"Prisoners?" asked the voice again. "Is this what you think of my hospitality?"

The voice was the woman's. She was lying in bed with the other. She was stroking his hair with one hand and feeding him grapes with the other. The one felt shot with a poisoned arrow laced with jealousy.

"Damn the other for being with her!" he thought. "It should be me!"

He could feel himself snarling inside. He wanted to be the one with her; he needed her.

"I should have eaten and drank with her," he thought, feeling anger and rage swelling toward the other.

As his glare softened, the one took notice of the other. Purple circles were appearing under his bloodshot eyes. His mouth was grizzled and chomped at the blood-red grapes like some dog fiending after stolen meat from the market. His skin took on a grainy green and red hue as his veins seemed to be rising out of his body like some drowning animal fighting their way to the surface. The one looked pleadingly at the other.

"Don't give me those looks, fool," snapped the other.

"Shh…" purred the woman as she stroked the other's hair. She sat up, chasing away the green satin sheets from her body. "He's hungry. Perhaps he needs a meal; or more sleep?"

The other reached to the plate on the mantle next to the bed and threw a fig at the one.

"Let the fool starve," he said as he chomped on a date.

"Come," said the woman as she playfully slapped the other, "sit with us."

She rose from the bed, leaning on one hand and extended her other hand toward the one. The one stood transfixed by the hand. He felt himself walking toward the bed. With every step she grew more terrifying and beautiful. With every stride, the pulsations of the amber glow grew in intensity, emerging, as it seemed, from this outstretched hand.

"You are safe here, young traveler. All the food and comforts you could possibly desire are here," she said above the snarling of the other. "Your troubles are over."

The throbbing glow overwhelmed the one's body. His heart fell into beat, as did the room itself. He reached for her hand, and when their fingers touched the haggard witch's face flashed before his eyes.

"Traveler!"

The one recoiled.

"I'm sorry," he stammered. "Perhaps I need to return to my bed."

The woman's eyes flashed violently. Her beauty seemed interrupted, impatient. The one began to step away from the woman as she gathered herself.

"Yes," she said. "A sleep would do you well."

The one turned to leave. He could feel her fiery eyes upon him as he walked toward to his room. He dared not turn around. As he limped off he felt a strange sensation come over him. The ravenous hunger he felt suddenly seemed to strengthen him somehow. He had yet to eat since being at the farm. His hunger had grown but he seemed to grow stronger, too. He also noticed feeling refreshed the longer he stayed awake. He had been asleep for days since arriving at the farm. He would awaken only to turn to the other side of the bed chasing after sleep. The more he slept the less refreshed he felt. But walking away from that room he felt an unusual strength rising out of his hunger and fatigue. He also thought about how the other looked: strung out and filled with rage.

"I need to leave this place," he whispered to himself.

The moment he gave it thought, however, he thought about the feast of food, the pool of water, and, of course, the haunting beauty of the woman. She terrified him. She allured him. There was also a kind of comfort he felt with her. Could he really leave her? Maybe he should go back and join her. He was lost in his plans to return to her after a nap when he stumbled into the room.

"You are not safe here," came the voice from the corner.

The voice was like ice water thrown in the face of a drunkard. Startled, he leapt back and searched fervidly for the voice. His eyes settled upon the darkened corner of the room, and he saw a haggard old woman hunched over, lighting a lantern.

"Excuse me," he said tentatively, "who are you?"

"Didn't you hear me, traveler?" shrieked the woman as she turned to face him. "You are not safe!"

The crumpled old hag had mismatched eyes, patchy hair, and a mouth of gangly, decaying teeth. Her face was pox-ridden with warts on her nose and chin. The one gasped at the sight of her, and before he could defend himself she was upon him. She grabbed his arm and dragged him behind her out the door and through the hallway, like a child would drag some ragdoll. With the other hand she held the lantern ahead. The lantern gave off a steady beam. The light seemed to change the walls. Sometimes they melted, other times they appeared to hide. And other times snakes would snap from the walls at the light. The one looked around in terror. Carcasses were tangled in spider webs and encoiled by constricting monsters. Ahead of them lay a doorway of bloodfire with a pale threshold. As they approached it, the flames reached higher and burned hotter. The walls of the hallway shot through with fire. The one slapped at her hand and cried out for her to stop. The hag dropped him to the ground like firewood and rounded on him.

"If you want to live, you will follow me. She will be onto you soon."

The hag stood tall now, her hunchback disappearing. The one marveled at the hag's strength. She had none of the appeal of the woman for whom he felt himself strangely longing. He looked back down the hallway and saw a carcass being devoured by a serpent. The sound of its jaw dislocating and the breaking of the carcass's bones made him sick. The amber glow from the room down the hallway now shot emerald green.

"But my friend," said the one as he panted heavily looking back to the hag. "We cannot leave him."

"He is no friend of yours," mocked the old hag.

The hag then appeared to soften as she spoke. She lowered her voice as if almost saddened. "He has fed upon too much of the woman's poison. He is too far gone. He cannot leave this place."

She looked to the threshold whose pale light started growing brighter. The flames shot at it like striking vipers. She stole a look back down the hallway and then wielded back upon him.

"You cannot save him, traveler. And if you don't leave with me, you won't be able to save yourself."

The one looked back over his shoulder. The amber glow was now fully engulfed in green flame. What looked like little spiders began darting outside the room and scurrying through the hallway toward them. He gave the hag a final pleading glance.

She reached out her hand, "Come, traveler," she said. "We must leave."

The one took her hand and followed her past the threshold, which the flames had nearly engulfed. The pale light was now all ablaze. As they crossed, a searing pain shot through the one's body. He felt his flesh burn, and his stomach wretch. The hag drew out what looked like a thistled herb from her pouch.

"You must eat this. You've been starved long enough."

The hag's face seemed to glow in the light of the lantern and her frail body filled with force. He looked to her and felt a slow burning sensation pass through his body, like coming in from the cold. She unsettled him. But she warmed him. He felt company for the fist time with her. He wasn't sure if he wanted her company, but it was the feeling of actually being with someone else that felt new. Her eyes widened at him as he reached for the herb, and seemed to soften as he took it. Just as he put the herb in his mouth he heard a piercing scream.

"You!" shot the banshee cry from down the hallway.

The one flashed around and saw the woman with the other standing next to her. Her beauty looked punctured. She had grown more terrible. A green light exploded around her and seemed to chase after the light of the lantern. The two met in a spectacular crash over the threshold. The monsters on the wall hissed violently and disappeared as the green mist engulfed the hallway. The other gnashed his teeth at the sight of the one. His face looked lacerated, and blood crusted around his lips.

"Run!" called the hag as she grabbed his arm and led him into the night.

The two ran until a large explosion threw them forward. The one felt thorns and rocks tear into the flesh of his knees and arms. Blood gushed from the cuts. His stomach and throat burned from the herb. He felt his pulse bursting from his head. He turned and saw the farm ablaze in a spectacular fire of green flame. He heard the curses and cries of the other along with the panicked squeals of the animals. The woman kicked through the walls and let out a monstrous roar. Flames danced around her like some pagan chorus. She flashed her head rhythmically to the dancing of the flames shouting in rage. The other shook his fists toward the two and cursed aloud. The one stumbled to his feet and tried to turn to run back to the other but the hag stopped him, squeezing his hand.

"Traveler," she said with surprising warmth. "You cannot save him."

The one gave a half-hearted tug with his arm, and the hag held him closer.

"He cannot cross the threshold. He's too far gone."

The one surveyed the burning farm and saw the other crawling to the threshold like some whimpering thing. He looked like a caged animal: scared, injured, violent. His body started to eviscerate as he broke the threshold. His screams became pig-like; his eyes flashed with terror as his body slowly metamorphosized into a wild boar. The spiders greedily devoured the dripping flesh hanging from the spawned boar, which squealed in horror.

"No!" cried the one as he reached out his hand against the constraining embrace of the hag.

He then saw the woman's flesh fall to the ground like an evening gown. Her eyes twisted and flashed green when, suddenly, her body morphed into a serpentine monster larger and more fierce than any he saw on the wall. Her beauty dripped away like the wax of a melting candle— each drop into the inferno spawning a terrible crawling thing.

The one felt the hag pull him.

The night all around shone black except for the lapping green flames rending the night apart like the breaking of glass. The green flame appeared halo-like over the writhing monster. The sound of her roars and the animals' screams shook the one. His body felt porous, as if an evil were passing through him. He fell to the ground retching, transfixed by the horror. He could no longer make out the threshold. The whole farm was asway in green flame. It seemed to respond to the roars of the dragon. Her body moved and the flames responded as if directed by some enchantment, some conductor's baton.

The burning farm snapped at the dark sky like a whip. Seeing it aroused an anxiety in him. He suddenly felt the presence of the hag and the burning of the herb. Relief and rage flashed together. He whipped the spittle from his mouth and spat upon the ground.

"What is this place?" he asked with a measure of defiance.

"It doesn't matter what this place is, traveler. You do not belong here."

Her voice faded for a moment. "Neither did he. But now he belongs nowhere. Come. We must go."

The voice felt like a new morning, and hearing it was like feeling the warm sun on one's face after a long winter. It sounded like the pouring of water, and it brought refreshment and healing. The burning herb began to taper and turned to tingling.

The one turned and saw the hag dash three stones onto the wildness ground. A flash of white exploded and cracked the darkness. The thorns and rock seemed to melt and a level path, bending west, became illuminated by a pale light. The one began to tremble as he looked to the hag. Her grey garments began to swirl with the flashing stones as she became engulfed in light and a rushing wind. Her hand reached out from the whirlwind and the one took it. He felt an energy fill his weary body. A great pressure pressed against his eyes and ears, like he had sunk into a deep abyss, when suddenly a sphere of blinding white engulfed the two with a muffled blast.

Then silence.

He looked back and saw the flaming farm. It looked like a land of corpses with phantom guards. The green mist danced around the writhing monster. She screamed out threats, but nothing could pierce the sphere. He looked for the other but he couldn't recognize him amidst the other animals scurrying away from the monster.

He turned again to the hag. She was no more. Or, she was different. Her hair was like a thick spindle of wool, colored by the darkest night. Her skin was bronze and her teeth the color of an ewe's milk. Her tattered grey garments were now cream with a golden sheen. She stood as tall as him, her body fully formed. The one fell to the ground and shielded his eyes with his hand. The pressure in his eyes became overbearing as he tried to rub out the irritation violently. There was some pain his fingers scratched at but couldn't reach.

"Your eyes are adjusting, traveler," said the woman.

The one scratched at his eyes. It felt like they were being eaten away by some acid. He screamed in agony and cursed at the woman.

"What have you done to me?" he shrieked. "Get this out of me!"

The one's eyes flushed with tears as he writhed on the wilderness floor. All he could see were flashes of green and white, and his head felt crushed between the two forces. His ears began to bleed, and he was coughing up blood.

"Your are adjusting," repeated the voice of the woman.

His coughing became more violent. Blood and bile began to come out together. He felt a rupture in the back of his head. The night paused as he fell slowly toward the ground. He seemed to float momentarily. A bursting glow of ivory shot through the night sky. He felt a great surge of heat against the side of his face. He turned his head and saw a green flame billowing at the sphere from the mouth of the dragon. Its muffled screams roused him for a moment as he floated downward toward the ground. A tear formed in his reddened eye as he looked upon the dragon. The serpent disappeared behind a glowing blast of light, and then all went black as he hit the ground with a thud.

Flashes of the path went through the one's eyes. He felt carried by some current, some stream, some wind. He looked down to the ground and saw the pale white path set off by the barren wilderness. Then black again.

The burning farm came to him during his sleep; then the woman with the dancing green eyes. She seemed to sing to him. Her song hurt the one, like the hearing of some funeral dirge. All her fierceness was gone. She came to him like a maiden; soft, delicate, pure. The one reached out his hand toward her but only felt stone as he was jarred awake.

The one then felt the woman's firm hand upon his shoulder as she led him to his feet.

"You must stay awake," she said as she handed him another herb.

The irritation throughout his body turned to a tingling. His eyes and ears shivered, like a mouth after the taste of honey. He looked at her with fear and wonder as she led him upon the illuminated path.

"I have carried you as far as I can," she said. "You must walk from here. It will strengthen you."

The hearing of her voice felt like the reminder of some

distant secret. Her appearance grew younger the further they journeyed. His legs were like those of a newborn horse; falling and stumbling, but growing in strength with each step. Still, every now and then he would fall to his knees and get sick.

"It's the poison," the woman would say. "Your body is getting rid of the toxins you have been breathing."

The woman handed him another herb. It tasted sweeter than the last one, and the thistles felt velvety and less prickly. He felt her hand reach for his. Her touch was soft and smooth and set off a charge through his body. She smelled like a garden in bloom and he was overcome with her grandeur. He couldn't resist the sight of her. Like a child who looks at the sun for the fist time, he could neither bear the sight nor turn from her. She weakened him. She strengthened him. She undid him. He felt re-created by her.

The two walked in long silence. Their hands touching ignited him, relieving him. Holding her hand felt like leaning up against a strong pillar. Her movements were sure and quick. Her gait was like that of a lioness. She glistened amidst the void of the wilderness as her gown flowed elegantly behind.

"I love you," he bumbled.

The woman's grip tightened around his hand as she let out a playful laugh.

"We have a long journey ahead of us, traveler."

The one's face shot red. Hearing "us" filled his heart. He stroked the woman's hand with his thumb and felt her hand gently squeeze his. He turned and considered the path ahead of him. He looked upon the pale light it emanated and was startled by memories of the threshold. He turned his eyes and looked on either side of the path and recoiled in horror. Scorpions crawled over fallen bodies, as jackals disemboweled them. Vultures swooped in, screeching and snapping for their share. The one felt lightheaded and the irritation in his eyes and ears returned. He bent over, and then dropped to a knee. The path grew dim and more bodies appeared, littered throughout the wilderness. Some of the bodies were still moving as the animals ripped into their flesh. The one bent over and retched up blood. He looked up for the woman but there was only grey. The way had disappeared and all that was left was the swirling wilderness. His blood and bile started to bubble, and stinging serpents emerged. He looked at the eviscerated bodies and thought he heard screams for help. Images of the other stretched across the threshold flashed through his mind. He heard his screams, the ripping of his flesh.

He looked ahead and saw the woman with the dancing green eyes. She was sitting by a table she had prepared. It was filled with meats and vegetables. Her eyes flashed as she looked upon the death scattered around her. She was wearing a dark emerald cloak that she dropped to the earth which turned into a giant serpent. The serpent slithered toward the bodies, swallowing them as it glided over the rocky floor. With each body consumed it grew, leaving a path of lush green behind it. Flowers began to bloom in its wake. The one looked to the woman who was beckoning him with her curling finger. He felt his stomach soothed at her sight. He reached out his hand and felt a searing slap across his face and a sudden flash of light.

The woman's face flickered and then vanished as he began to feel he was being devoured from the inside. He curled up in agony. His body flashed with heat and then cold as the wilderness went black.

In the blackness he felt nothing. He heard the gliding serpent slithering toward him, feeling it coil itself around him. The serpent constricted its mighty coils. He felt his joints dislocate and his blood vessels break. He thought to scream but a calm overtook him. Images of the woman in white came to his mind and he longed for her. But he was weary and ready for that final rest. The nothingness would be better than this, he thought. His heart slowed its beat as he lost all thought. His breath left him as the serpent opened its mouth and began to slide over him. All was gone now. All was done. All was quiet. But in the darkness he awoke. Everything was amber and cramped; like a dying fire being suffocated to sleep. He felt pinned and his throat constricted. He tried to scream but he had no voice.

Suddenly, a pinhole of light pierced through the darkness. It widened until he felt a stab into his heart. It felt like fire was being poured down his throat. His limbs crackled and snapped back into joint. His eyes opened fully to the sight of the woman in white. Her lips were upon his, and her breath passed through his empty lungs. His chest rose as it filled with her breath. He sprang up coughing. He felt her embrace and her hand pressing against his back.

"You wandered off the path," he heard her voice say.

He pulled himself up and she sat him against a small rock. The woman had made a small fire and fed him more herbs. They felt thistled again, and burned his stomach as he ate them. He heard the twigs snap in the flame as the woman tended it. She was making some liquid with the herbs and made him drink it.

"Was I dreaming?" asked the one, darting his eyes in alarm as he looked for the serpent.

"You must not wander off the path," said the woman as she

coupled his head in her arm helping him drink.

The one looked into her eyes and was filled with remorse. How could I leave this woman, he thought? He felt her warmth against his shivering body and grew calm. He looked ahead and saw the pale path again. He looked to the wilderness and felt the woman's hand jerk his head forward.

"You must keep to the path," she said.

The one slurped the liquid the woman had made for him. It tasted foul but calmed his churning stomach. He held onto the woman with his weakened grip fearing if he let go she would be lost.

"Where are we going?" he asked as he peered down the distance of the path.

The woman lifted her hand with his and pointed westward over the mountains.

"There," she said. "That is where you are going."

"Where?" asked the one. "I don't see anything."

"To the city," intoned the woman. "You will see it soon enough."

"The city?" gasped the one with a note of fear. "And what do you mean 'you will see it soon enough'? Aren't you coming along?"

The woman smiled.

"Yes, traveler, the city. I will be with you, but this is a trip you must make."

The one looked puzzled. He thought about the city. Fragments of some memory began to assemble in his mind only to break apart.

"What is this place like?" he asked holding on to her.

"It's a great city," she said as her eyes danced. "With a giant tree that is always in season. It stands in the center of the city and gives it shade and life. A great fountain lies underneath the tree and nourishes the city."

Hearing of the city again quickened some memory in the one. Like the rush of blood to limbs long asleep, his head began to sparkle with the forming of images and feelings long past. He looked into the flame and forms of faces began to take shape—faces that seemed familiar. He was lost in the long silence. Looking into the flame was like puzzling over some ancient manuscript. The characters fascinated him, but he couldn't read their mysteries. The fire crackled and chased away the faces. He turned to the woman and saw her watching him.

"She, the woman…or, whatever she was…is she gone?" the one stammered cautiously, breaking the fragile silence.

It was now the woman's turn to turn to the fire. She fiddled with a stick and threw it into the flame.

"No. She is not gone. She is never gone," she said, rapidly wiping her hands free of the earth.

"She's like a plague that never dies nor disappears for good. She can lie dormant. But even in her absence she preys upon travelers who wander through the wilderness. The city protects us, but she broods over these lands like a threat. Eventually her venom will rise again, poisoning the wells and soil and covering them with her thorns. She spreads her wilderness everywhere."

The one dropped his head at this hearing.

"Gone but never gone," he lamented.

The woman smiled and gave him another herb. It tasted like honey this time and lifted his spirits.

"Eat, traveler. You have escaped her prison but the poison is still in you."

The woman looked at the man as if measuring him when a smile broke across her face. She seemed to grow in stature and power. Her face shone clear like a mountain stream, and her smile split the grey of the wilderness like the rising sun. She rose to her feet and stood over the one.

A golden ray of light emitted from her mouth and slowly crawled toward the one. When it reached him, it passed into his mouth. The one at first tried to fight it but it overcame him—like the coils of the monster but different. His body felt like it was brought out of a damp cave and into the sun of a warm day. A radiant light burst from the woman blinding the one from her.

"Take this," he heard her voice say. "You left it long ago."

The light then collapsed into a parchment, which floated downward toward the path. The woman was nowhere to be found. The one called for her. A shiver went through his body as he again felt alone. He shouted until he could taste blood in the back of his throat.

"Follow the path," whispered the voice upon the breeze.

The one shouted again after her. "Take me with you!" he cried.

The one shouted and cursed at the voice until he fell to
his knees. The one wept, punching the ground. The breeze
returned, cooing like some love might. The one opened
his eyes and saw the face of the woman in the breeze. Her
hand reached to his face and held it. She smiled and leaned
to kiss the one. The breeze broke upon his lips, engulfing
his body. The breeze felt like the shade on a summer's day.
His body quickened, and the company of the woman once
more could be felt.

"I've gone ahead of you, traveler," whispered the breeze,
and then floated up the path toward the mountains and
the city on the other side of the wilderness.

The one watched the breeze along the path. Its pale light
growing brilliant as it passed. He felt the parchment blow
up against his feet and bent over to pick it up. He unfurled
it slowly, not wanting to rip it or awaken something slum-
bering inside. The one stretched the parchment and held it
to the fire. At first it looked like a vinegar stained canvass
with rips and creases threatening its composition. As
he held it to the fire, images and scratchings started to

manifest themselves. It was a tattered map. Startled, he looked up from the map and surveyed the wilderness to make sure it was safe to proceed with the map, guarding it like some secret. A chill slowly trickled through his body as a familiarity dawned over him. Had he seen this map before?

Scratched on the map were markings of some kind. As if awoken by some magic, the light of the fire revealed what appeared to be the notations of a surveyor. The map sparkled with records of temperatures and elevations, depths of rivers and cycles of the moon, orbits of the planets and positions of the stars. The script along the map was elegant and crisp, like some ancient scribe had adorned a sacred text. Every detail appeared aware of its surroundings, fussing after the smallest detail of the terrain.

As the one read the writing, it seemed to etch the rough outlines of some memory; some journey he had been on long ago. Flashes of a forest and a stream came to his mind. Images of lush fields, crystal skies, and a kind of plenty shot through his memory like a twinkle in a lover's eye.

He studied the map further and noticed it was incomplete. The map had not been fully drawn. He turned the map and held it closer to the fire. Writing, as if scrawled by a drunken hand, started to take shape near the hinterlands of the unmarked parchment. Gone was the beauty and care of the script. He felt his pulse rise and an arising alarm as he fervidly pressed the parchment as near the flame as his hands would allow.

"Some danger here..." read the drunken writing with some string of words as it trailed off.

The one recoiled in horror when he recognized the handwriting, dropping it to the ground.

"Impossible," he gasped.

Deep in the night he heard again the whisper of the woman upon the breeze. He leaned his head back, closed his eyes and with outstretched arms drew the cool night air deep into his lungs. Something purifying, a kind of purging energy seemed to pass through him. He bent over to pick up the map once more. He squinted again at the notes and realized that he must have wandered from the path many years ago. He had been on some kind of journey but became lost and entrapped by some magic. Images of the farm and prison flashed before his eyes. Semblances of early memories in the prison knifed through his mind. He looked again to the map and saw where he was. His body was all alive now; all awake. He rolled up the map and looked around the wilderness. The night was crisp. He could hear the animals scurrying around the wilderness floor. He could smell the decay. And he could see the path clear as sunshine reflecting off a freshly fallen snow. Everything around him popped. He put the rolled-up parchment into his pocket and looked to the path that led through the mountains to the city. The one wiped his chin, and took his first steps toward the city on the other side of the wilderness.

ESSAY:

THE ROMANCE OF THE OTHER SIDE

Safety Not Guaranteed

I begin this essay with the comedic critique of French dating sites by the French moral philosopher, Alain Badiou. Badiou lists several of the advertisements—e.g., "Get love without chance!"; "Be in love without falling in love!"; and, "Get perfect love without suffering!"—and notes how this language not only misses what love is, but perverts it into something it cannot be: that is, risk free.[1] Though the rise of dating sites is an intriguing trend, one could be forgiven for cynically seeing them as little more than virtual Yentas or part of the matchmaking game that has long been part of human pairing. But what is decidedly new about this move is its attempt to engineer love through proclaimed discourses of science. The basic elements of "love" have been broken down into their separable parts so as to allow for their genetically modified rearrangement. The dynamics are eerily similar to that of eugenics: we trim and crop the undesirable, aided by science and sophisticated algorithms, of course, all in the name of the betterment of our species. After all, what could possibly be better than love? This introduction of a "safety-first concept of love," a love with comprehensive insurance protecting those on the dating highways against all risk and wreckage, is, according to Badiou, "disturbing." [2] For "love cannot be a gift given on the basis of a complete lack of risk." [3]

These criticisms are part of his wider project of extending Rimbaud's axiom that "love needs re-inventing." Love needs re-inventing precisely because of love's presence within a world full of "new developments." Badiou sees safety and comfort as the two enemies of love. New developments in the world introduce new ways in which safety and comfort inscribe themselves into these new worlds. Love must therefore always be the act of re-description lest it be overtaken by safety and comfort in their new guises.

Rather counter-intuitively, what at first sounds like an enemy of safety and comfort manifests itself as their fiercest ally: the loveless profligate. The traveling businessman and his wondering hands at the cocktail bar might sound

like anything but safe and comfortable, but his long list of
conquests testify to precisely that. The profligate is the self
turned in on itself. Love is the self turned outward. Love is
therefore not absent from pleasure; it is the presence that
fills absences with pleasure. As Gillian Rose said so well,

> Nothing is foreign to [love]; it tarries with the nega-
> tive; it dallies with the mundane, and it is ready for
> the unexpected.[4]

Simone de Beauvoir, in her book, *The Second Sex*, gives
expression to the disenchanted post-coital scene. As Badiou
reads her, "after having sex, the man feels the woman's
body is flat and flabby and the woman feels in parallel that
the man's body, apart from his erect member, is generally
unattractive, if not slightly ridiculous."[5] The promise of
seduction is the enchantment of the other but not *as an
other*. The other becomes broken down into fetishized
objects: "breasts, buttocks, and cock."[6] It is this stark shift
from enchantment to disenchantment within the seduction
of the profligate that the Hebrew Proverbs aptly described
as "first the honey, then the gravel;" or what Rose calls the
morning of "holy terror."[7]

Love, however, focuses on the other *as an other*; "on the other as it has erupted, fully armed with its being, into my life thus disrupted and refashioned."[8] This is why love is the true enemy of the safe and comfortable. Whereas the promiscuous promise collapses back into the safe and the comfortable precisely because it collapses back into the self, love erupts into the wild and risky dissolution of the self. Love destroys the self, refashioning it in light of the other. It challenges our lives from the perspective of difference. Love is therefore a deferment of the self to include a perspective outside of self. [9] To love, for Badiou, is therefore to quest after wisdom. To be open to love is to be open to wisdom; to consider a world experienced from "the point of view of two and not one."[10]

Perhaps this is what Plato meant when he suggested that "anyone who doesn't take love as a starting point will never understand the nature of philosophy." Love unsettles the constructed world of singularities, be they solipsisms or empires. It is the possibility of always being present at the birth of the world. Love is the witness, the testimony, to the creation which itself testifies to our creatureliness and thus to the truth beyond truth, the other side of truth, the way of wisdom.

This eruption is owing to the duality of love. Love "involves a separation or disjuncture based on the simple difference between two people and their infinite subjectivities."[11] It separates, dislocates, and differentiates one from oneself. But it is "precisely because it encompasses a disjuncture," that at that moment when one and one become two and see the world in a new way, the world itself is reborn.[12] This is what Rose has called the third partner, or "the work;"[13] and what Badiou has called the *Two Scene:* life being made "no longer from the perspective of the One but from the perspective of Two."[14] The playboy at the cocktail bar, or the seductress on the street never get beyond the encounter and thus recapitulate the world in its givenness—the world as safe and comfortable. But love erupts from the encounter, constructing a world in its wreckage, and unleashing the self on a "tenacious adventure" away from itself and into possibility.[15] Love is therefore a re-invention of life when the self is in confrontation with the life of the other.

The intimacies of the seductress or playboy and those of love are not necessarily visibly different. The surrender of the body to the frontiers of pleasure, the ritualized disrobing and pressing of flesh to flesh, the rehearsing of the body's erotic rhythms and movements, the sounds and variations of speed and intensity all may appear the same. But in the case of the former, as Lacan might say, the individual is on its own. Though bodies are penetrating and being penetrated, pleasure is valorizing the self into its own deeper recesses. The body of the other is a mediation for the pleasure of the self. But the wild delirium and transportation of pleasure within love's bedroom does not collapse back onto the fragile self. "Love-making is never simply pleasure."[16] Exhausted and tangled bodies with panting breath are declarations, the audible venerations, of love's presence. The pleasure of the playboy is the choice of the safe and comfortable; the acceptance of the current staging of the world. The pleasure of the lover is the penetration of the lie, the undressing of the old order and the construction of new life. The orgasm of the seductress is the sound of retreat. Love's orgasm is a battle cry. To f**k is to forget. To love is to subvert.[17]

Love not only undresses the world of givennenss, but it also questions the hegemony of meaning which can amount to little other than meaninglessness. The life of safety and comfort are only safe and comfortable insofar as they are lived within the spaces of power's fictive providence. Power names the encounter of events as meaningful, and these events are meaningful only if we accept power's naming of them as such. But love introduces real contingency, and the randomness of events that destabilize the reach of empire's constructed world. But here love itself becomes vulnerable. How "can what is pure chance at the outset become the fulcrum for a construction of truth?"[18] This is what separates the profligate and the lover. The profligate fails at getting himself beyond contingency, whereas love transforms contingency into a creation which lasts, allowing for the event to be viewed retroactively as the work of providence. The chance encounter of the promiscuous includes in itself its own ending. After orgasm, first the blush, then the exit. The contingency in love's encounter, however, "morphs into the assumption of a beginning." The third partner, in Rose's estimation, Love's work, "equalizes the emotions, and enables the two submerged to surface in a series of unpredictable configurations. Work is the constant carnival; words, the rhythm and pace of the two, who mine undeveloped seams of the earth and share the treasure."[19] The declaration of love's realization, in the words of Badiou, is to "embark on a construction of truth," where contingency and chance are at last curbed, and power's facile world is questioned. Chance becomes destiny precisely where the new world erupts out of the naked and old world.[20]

Because the profligate includes his own end within the event itself, he introduces a serialization of events that collapse into randomness. But to love is to commit "to construct something that will endure in order to release the encounter from its randomness."[21] This is fidelity: the movement from random encounter to necessity; from the acceptance of the world that is given to the birth of a new one. *Love is revolution.*

Badiou suggests that "love that is real is always of interest to the whole of humanity."[22] There is something ubiquitous about the appeal of the love story. It is precisely the interest in the love story that is itself so interesting. Caught up in our own comfort and safety, we cannot help but observe others living the danger and ecstasy of love. From the comforts of our own homes and theaters, we cannot turn away from the love story's undressing of our world in the creation of its own. We now come full circle to where we began. As Badiou says, "the process of love isn't always peaceful." It has its own "contradictions and violence." [23] The great tales of love are not all innocence, happiness, and romance; they are equally tragedy, rejection, and rage. The wonder of the love story, however, is its "exploration of the abyss separating individuals and the description of the fragile nature of the bridge that love throws between two solitudes." [24] On the rickety bridge of love, safety cannot be guaranteed.

Wisdom's Romance

The book of Proverbs can be seen as a love story from this perspective. We are to court the ways of wisdom in response to her overtures. We pursue wisdom because wisdom is pursuing us. The romantic descriptions of the way of the man with his maiden also reflect the relationship we are to have with insight and understanding. "Let her breasts satisfy you at all times; let her love intoxicate you" (5:19). Experiencing and exploring the otherness of the beloved, giving oneself over to the intoxicating eroticisms of naked communion, is not simply language of romantic human partnerships. It is the romance of wisdom. It is a tale of deferment to an other, an escape from the deep individual abyss of the one and the allowance of difference through the constructed world of the two (12:15; 14:12). The destructive way that seems right to the one is exposed in the romance of the two (16:25). Wisdom is like a "master worker" (8:30), and wherever her romance is present, new creations, new worlds, emerge.

Jean-Luc Nancy masterfully called love a kind of "abandonment."[25] It is the deferment of the perspective of the one toward otherness—"the extreme movement beyond the self," and into the grand gestures of more.[26] It is this *more* where wisdom lives and where wisdom takes us. But first it must break us.[27] Love is the *more*, the other, forever disjoining the self from itself. The thousand ships launched by love dash themselves upon the jagged rocks of the everyday, loosing an infinity of shatters which enchant the everyday with the promise of more, cutting across identity and leaving a wound for and from which otherness can grow. "Love forms the limit of a thinking that carries itself to the limit" of all thinking; to where "thinking extricates itself" and wisdom reaches back.[28] This extraction is the self's crossing to the other side—to the way of wisdom.

How can we possibly understand our own way (20:24)? Perhaps we understand ourselves too much. As Jean-Luc Nancy says, "there is in fact too much identity" alive today.[29] Love must therefore be destructive. A shattering. A refusal of the arrived, and "pure arriving."[30] Those who live their lives on the stage of one are fools (29:26). Those who give themselves over to the romance of wisdom, those who respond to her overtures, those who pursue her, live the life of the two and cross over the rickety little bridge to the other side along the way of wisdom. These are the ones who discover more, the ones who live life abundantly.

LOVE-RELATED PROVERBS

Proverbs 8:10-11

Take my instruction instead of silver, and knowledge rather than choice gold, for wisdom is better than jewels, and all that you may desire cannot compare with her.

WHAT ARE YOUR EYES GROPING FOR?

Proverbs 12:25

Anxiety in a man's heart weighs him down, but a good word makes him glad.

WHAT VOICE
ARE YOU
LISTENING TO?

Proverbs 13:12

Hope deferred makes the heart sick,
but a desire fulfilled is a tree of life.

WHAT TURN OF EVENT IS
YOUR HEART WAITING UPON?

A desire fulfilled is sweet to the
soul, but to turn away from evil is
an abomination to fools.

HOW DO YOUR COMPULSIONS EXPOSE YOU?

Proverbs 15:17

Better is a dinner of herbs where
love is than a fattened ox and
hatred with it.

ARE LOVING RELATIONSHIPS ENOUGH FOR YOU?

RA-10194-D

Proverbs 15:30

The light of the eyes rejoices
the heart, and good news
refreshes the bones.

WHO ARE YOU LOOKING AND LISTENING TO?

Proverbs 16:24

Gracious words are like a
honeycomb, sweetness to the soul
and health to the body.

ARE YOUR WORDS
MORE THAN
MERELY EDIBLE?

Proverbs 17:9

Whoever covers an offense seeks love, but he who repeats a matter separates close friends.

WILL YOU **SHUT YOUR MOUTH** TO SAVE **FRIENDSHIPS?**

Proverbs 17:17

A friend loves at all times,
and a brother is born for adversity.

Proverbs 17:22

A joyful heart is good medicine,
but a crushed spirit dries up the bones.

HOW ARE YOU CARING FOR YOUR MOST SENSITIVE AND VITAL ORGAN?

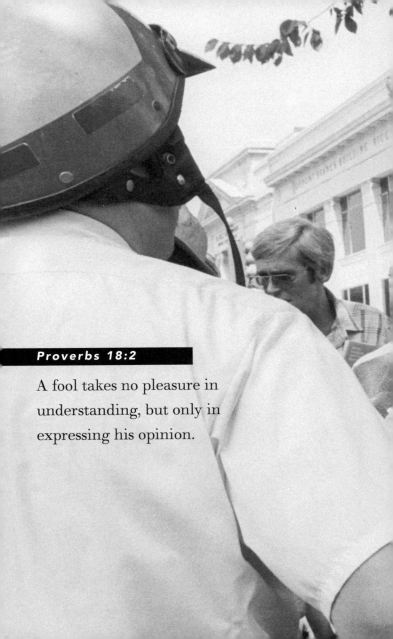

Proverbs 18:2

A fool takes no pleasure in
understanding, but only in
expressing his opinion.

**What feels better to you:
self-expression or understanding?**

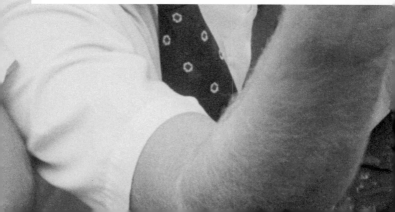

He who finds a wife finds
a good thing and obtains
favor from the Lord.

Proverbs 19:8

Whoever gets sense loves his own
soul; he who keeps understanding
will discover good.

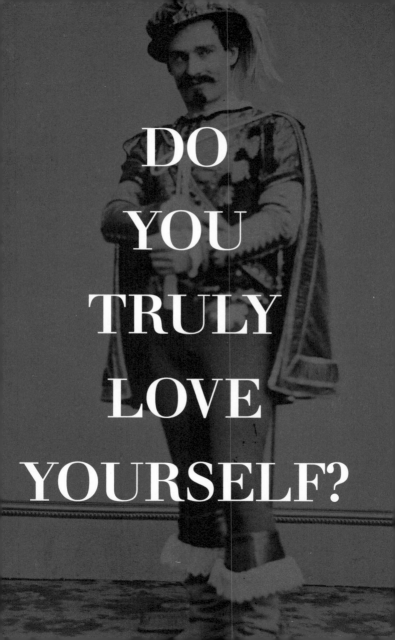

Proverbs 19:22

What is desired in a man is
steadfast love, and a poor man
is better than a liar.

WHAT DO YOU LOOK FOR IN A MAN?

Proverbs 20:6

Many a man proclaims his own steadfast love, but a faithful man who can find?

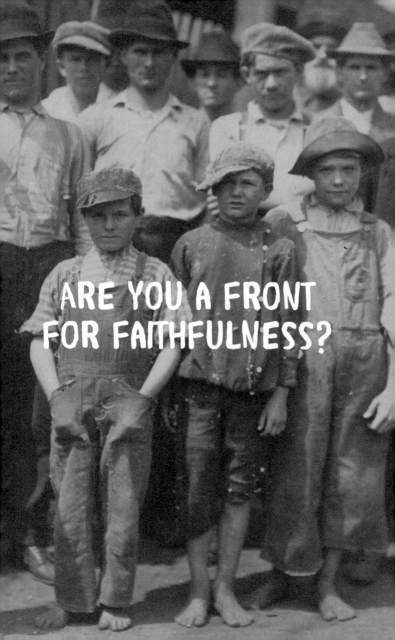

Proverbs 21:17

Whoever loves pleasure will be a
poor man; he who loves wine and
oil will not be rich.

Proverbs 24:13-14

My son, eat honey, for it is good,
and the drippings of the honeycomb are sweet
to your taste. Know that wisdom is such to your
soul; if you find it, there will be a future, and
your hope will not be cut off.

HOW DOES WISDOM TASTE TO YOU?

Whoever gives an honest
answer kisses the lips.

Are you a great kisser?

Proverbs 27:5

Better is open rebuke than
hidden love.

What good is your muted love?

121

Proverbs 29:3

He who loves wisdom makes his
father glad, but a companion of
prostitutes squanders his wealth.

ARE YOUR
AFFECTIONS
BUILDING A LEGACY
OR LEADING TO
SQUALOR?

PART THREE: HORROR

ESSAY:

THE PERIL OF THE OTHER SIDE

The Horror! The Horror!

It has been said that there are only so many stories one can tell. Across cultures and time, groupings of the long list of stories we have told emerge within discernable patterns. Stories take on provincial nuance to be sure, as what is funny or scary, for example, are recognized in distinct ways across cultures. But the fact that there are a handful of genres that appear to be fairly widespread across the narrations of humanity is quite extraordinary. The particulars of these narrations vary from culture to culture, but certain genres tend to appear wherever the human animal tells stories. We are *homo narrans*.

One of these seemingly universal genres is horror. What is it about us that is drawn to being scared? Why do we subject ourselves to the spectacle of horror? Or is this even

the right way of putting it? Perhaps we should first begin by
asking why such narratives exist? Horror stories should "be
examined within the intricate matrix of relations (social,
cultural, and literary-historical) which generate them."[1] As
the anthropologist Mary Douglas rightly noted, feelings of
disgust and fear, or aversion to apparent transgressions or
violations makes sense only within specific cultural categories.[2] The horror genre might then be usefully seen as
not necessarily fitting within the conceptual scheme of one
sort, but in violation of it.[3] But why do we tell scary stories?

This has been the subject of much theorizing from the likes
of Freud to a host of contemporary theorists.[4] Perhaps such
stories are safe exercises of our most foreboding socio-cul-
tural fears? Freud himself suggested that "uncanny expe-
riences" mark the return to consciousness of repressed
infantile complexes. Or, following Douglas, we might see
the horror story as a group exercise in social norms and
categories. We might even press here for specificity as to
what kind of horror story we are talking about. Within
the horror genre, there are many subgenres: demonic,
alien, monster, slasher, and so on. Stephen Asma suggests
that "stories about monster threats and heroic conquests

provide us with a ritualized, rehearsable simulation of reality, a virtual way to represent the forces of nature, the threats from other animals, and the dangers of human social interaction."[5] There are also elements in which horror might crop up in other genres without that story being classified as horror.

Latent within most horror stories is a breach of some kind. A party is wronged, a spirit is disturbed, or as in the case of the original *Gojira* (1954), hubris has crossed nature's lines. The unfolding plot often takes the form as an attempt to heal that breach. It is this breach, along with what the noted film theorist Mario Rodriguez has described as the social commentary the horror genre gives,[6] that I would like to consider.

This breach communicates a fundamental unease and imbalance within the symbol system and narrative world. Something, someone, some force, has been upset, unsettled, and is loosed for vengeance. The perception of this breach introduces crises into the story. In *Hamlet*, that great story of vengeance, we get a sense of this foreboding early when Marcellus reports to Horatio after the appearance of the haunting ghost, "something is rotten in the state of Denmark." The haunting specter disjoints time—or, better, the vengeful spirit is loosed through the fissures of the breach caused by Claudius' fratricide. The very presence of the horror genre, or elements of horror within other genres, demonstrates at least the threat of the world's dissolution.

The world in which we live is sustained and maintained through a complex network of rituals and rules. This network is fluid, even allowing for its own forms of trespass and rebooting, as in the phenomena of Saturnalia or carnival, or the scapegoat. But it is when this network is disrupted *outside* these allowable forms of purification and trespass that horror resides. Horror is guided by a series of balances and imbalances. The movement from one to the other and back again not only drives the plot, but also alerts us to the fragility of our world, the reality of threats to our world, and the importance of rituals and rules for its maintenance. The plot and drive toward resolution within the horror genre is thus more than simply healing this breach; it is the attempt to rebuild one's world.

There are, as stated above, many aspects and elements of

horror. In classical stories like *Godzilla*, there is an ambiguity introduced with respect to the label of "monster." Who, or what, is the monster in this story? Is it the giant radioactive reptile emerging from the depths of the sea? Or is it the hubris of science's careless courting of nature? We might also ask this of *Frankenstein* as well: Who is the monster? Is it the creature or the scientist who created it? The culpability of the carnage and wreckage wrought in these two stories is brilliantly ambiguated—not only the culpability, but the very identities of the players involved. It may be perhaps too much to say that the roles of protagonist and antagonist get reversed in such stories, but they do get blurred. To put the question rather perversely: which is more "monstrous": the "monsters" who emerge or the conditions which create them? *Godzilla* and *Frankenstein* are not about gratuitous carnage from mindless monsters, but revenge and retaliation precisely where the maintenance of rituals and boundary rules were neglected. Horror, then, and the labeling of the monstrous, is utterly perspectival.

The Fool's Monstrosity

The book of Proverbs contains surprising and spectacular

elements of horror in this respect. Early in the book we read that the "simple are killed *by their turning away*, and *the complacency* of fools destroys them" (1:32). Within the horror genre, there appear to be a set of rules dictating whom will be killed throughout the story. These rules are often spoofed in such movies as *Scream* or *Cabin in the Woods*. The fool is often among the unlucky in such stories for breaking these rules. We might picture the "simple" here as the hapless stoner who wanders off on his own, turning away from the group to relieve him in some sort of way. Or the frisky couple who disappear into the dark for a quick exercise of their passions. Those who turn away or wander off are picked off like wounded animals by predators in horror films. The foolish—those who do not operate within the horror genre's rationality of wisdom and folly—are brutally murdered one by one. Their destruction in the horror genre allows for comedic relief in some cases, while allowing the killer to accrue power and foreboding. What is striking in Proverbs 1:32 is that though we do not know the immediate cause of the simpleton's death, what is clear is that the ultimate cause for the destruction of the fool and the simple is their own folly. And Wisdom, which was once crying aloud in the streets (1:20), now laughs and mocks the foolish in their death throes (1:26–27).

Zombie stories continue to grow in popularity. From Max Brooks' *War World Z*, to the hit TV show *The Walking Dead*, the story of the zombie is the story of a contagion—usually a scientific experiment or drug gone wrong—setting loose an epidemic of de-humanization. The terror of the genre is that it depicts the blind aggression and lethal capacities of the undead as a threat to the frailty of life. The undead are crazed with the insatiable need to feed. Proverbs depicts the foolish in zombie-like ways as those who are never satisfied or filled: always feeding yet never full (e.g., 27:20).

Elsewhere in Proverbs we read of the "forbidden woman" who, vampire-like, seduces the weak and drags them to hell (7:22–23; cf. 5:3–6; 22:14). The temptress in Proverbs is not necessarily evidence of a misogynistic view of women. Women are used throughout as personifications of the ways of wisdom (life) and folly (death) alike. The point is not gender politics but the way one follows. The way most consider right is actually the broad road to death (14:12). The call of Proverbs is to reject the illusion—the way of appearance that leads to death—and walk in the way of life. The vampire-like temptress feeding off the foolishness of the weak, has laid low many, and her lair lies on the way to Sheol. When she rises from her coffin, the life of the living is sucked from their bodies and brought down to the chambers of death (7:27).

The fool is also depicted as a ravenous monster. Blood-thirsty and hating the wise, these monsters stalk the life of the upright (29:10). They prey upon the poor of the earth, seeking to devour them with their sword-like teeth and knives for fangs (30:14). They are more dangerous than an attacking bear (17:12). Better to be cornered by the monstrous bear in *The Edge* (1997) than to be near the most dangerous animal of all: the fool.

The way of wisdom is the path through these balances and imbalances. As with the horror genre, all restorations of balance are temporary. When balance is restored, there is always the looming threat of return. We see this master-fully in the final paragraph of Camus' *The Plague*. The good Dr. Rieux listens to the cries of joy rising from the city when the imbalance of the plague was finally brought back into balance. But he knows that "such joy is always imperiled." He knew that

> the plague bacillus never dies or disappears for good;
> that it can lie dormant for years and years in furniture
> and linen-chests; that it bides its time in bedrooms,
> cellars, trunks, and bookshelves; and that perhaps the
> day would come when, for the bane and the enlight-
> ening of men, it would rouse up its rats again and send
> them forth to die in a happy city.[7]

The wisdom of Dr. Rieux is in seeing that even when the
horror recedes, there is always the threat of return. In
horror, there is never finality. Because life is lived between
these competing forces, there is always sequel. Life will
therefore always contain elements of horror. This is why
Wisdom lives within the imagery of journey, of life lived
along a path. Wisdom is never the once for all. It lives
within the choices of the everyday, threatened by horror
within the spaces of imbalance on every side. Folly stalks
wisdom just as wisdom stalks folly along the journey to
the other side.

HORROR-RELATED PROVERBS

Proverbs 7:22-23

All at once he follows her, as an ox goes
to the slaughter, or as a stag is caught
fast till an arrow pierces its liver; as a
bird rushes into a snare; he does not
know that it will cost him his life.

AS THE HUNTED, HOW WILL YOU
ESCAPE FROM BECOMING THE PREY?

Proverbs 14:1

The wisest of women builds her
house, but folly with her own hands
tears it down.

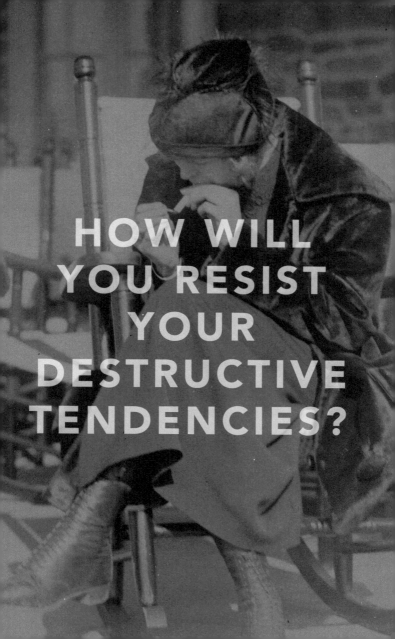

Proverbs 14:12

There is a way that seems right to a
man, but its end is the way to death.

Proverbs 17:12

Let a man meet a she-bear robbed of
her cubs rather than a fool in his folly.

ARE YOU LOOKING FOR TROUBLE?

Proverbs 17:13

If anyone returns evil for good,
evil will not depart from his house.

WHAT WRONGS FROM YOUR PAST ARE HAUNTING YOUR PRESENT?

The sluggard buries his hand in the dish and will not even bring it back to his mouth.

WHAT INDULGENCES DEADEN
YOUR MOTIVATION?

The terror of a king is like the
growling of a lion; whoever provokes
him to anger forfeits his life.

DO YOU WANT
TO STICK IT TO
"THE MAN"?

Bread gained by deceit is sweet to a
man, but afterward his mouth will
be full of gravel.

What are you afraid will
come back and bite you?

.

Proverbs 21:9

It is better to live in a corner of the housetop than in a house shared with a quarrelsome wife.

the other side

Proverbs 21:10

The soul of the wicked desires evil;

his neighbor finds no mercy in his eyes.

Can you identify the
sociopaths in your world?

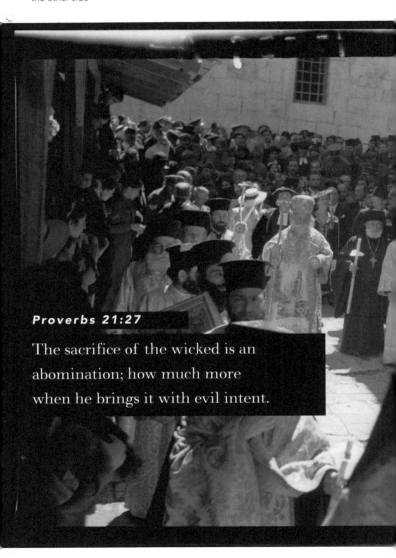

Proverbs 21:27

The sacrifice of the wicked is an
abomination; how much more
when he brings it with evil intent.

Proverbs 25:16

If you have found honey,
eat only enough for you,
lest you have your fill of it
and vomit it.

What abundance are you hoarding
that is making you sick?

Proverbs 25:19

Trusting in a treacherous man in
time of trouble is like a bad tooth
or a foot that slips.

Can we count on you to be who you appear
to be when we need you most?

Proverbs 25:26

Like a muddied spring or
a polluted fountain is a
righteous man who gives
way before the wicked.

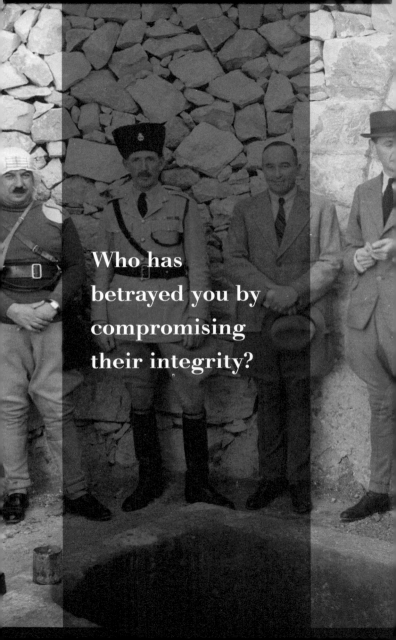

Who has
betrayed you by
compromising
their integrity?

Whoever sends a message by
the hand of a fool cuts off his
own feet and drinks violence.

**Who do you allow to represent
you and your interests?**

Proverbs 26:11

Like a dog that returns to his vomit
is a fool who repeats his folly.

Are you unwilling to see repeat offenders for what they are?

Like the glaze covering an earthen vessel
are fervent lips with an evil heart.

Proverbs 26:28

A lying tongue hates its victims,
and a flattering mouth works ruin.

Do you honestly think it is loving to lie or flatter?

Proverbs 27:20

Sheol and Abaddon are never satisfied, and never satisfied are the eyes of man.

What hole are you trying to fill?

Proverbs 30:17

The eye that mocks a father and scorns to obey a mother will be picked out by the ravens of the valley and eaten by the vultures.

HOW IMPORTANT ARE YOUR PARENTS?

PART FOUR: EPIC

ESSAY:

THE JOURNEY TO THE OTHER SIDE

So far we have considered wisdom from the perspective of the love story and the horror genre. I would now like to hazard an extension of these reflections on wisdom through the genre of epic. I am not suggesting that the Hebrew wisdom tradition in general, or the book of Proverbs in particular, is an epic—or, for that matter, that the genre of epic is even a stable concept. What I would like to suggest is that there are elements of epic scattered through Proverbs and that Proverbs itself participates within—while provoking the reader to participate within as well—a wider epic. Viewing Proverbs through the lens of epic, I suggest, will cast its collection of aphorisms into fresh relief.[1]

The trouble with words is that they lure us into simplicity, only to leave us with confusion. We use common words but often use them in uncommon ways. One such word with diverse usages and diffuse understandings is "epic."

Imagine a surfer fresh off the waves of Mavericks, California, speaking about her last ride and describing the wave. Or think of the comparative literature professor from Stanford summarizing to her students the history of the epic genre. Now imagine a group of teenage boys watching YouTube videos of "epic fails." This word would be thrown around well enough in each situation, but it might be difficult to get any sense of what *epic* actually means when these three contexts are taken together. In popular usage, as Paul Innes has suggested, anything relating to range, scope, and size has been described as epic.[2] If we are going to use this word, therefore, we will need to insert some measure of specificity.

The Mess of Homer's Brilliance

Genre, as we have suggested in the Introduction, is hardly a stable category with neatly policed boundaries. Each bleeds into the other. Regardless of how one defines epic, one thing is clear: it must begin with Homer. The repetitions of Virgil, Milton, and Joyce, and the ruminations by Hegel and Morrison, all operate within the brilliant wreckage loosed by the *Iliad* and the *Odyssey*. The towering genius of Homer was his discovery and formulation of an ideal cosmos and the population of that cosmos with actors and actresses, both human and divine, infused with a fire of purpose contained within the founding of a people. The action within the *Iliad* and the *Odyssey* carries within itself a sense in which the actors feel they have stepped or been invited into Homer's narrative world. They do not float in and out of Homer's created space. They exist here and nowhere else.

Ideal Worlds, Ideal Pasts

A significant aspect of epic is its sense of totality. An epic is a narration about ideal worlds, full and complete. These worlds are large enough to house the fullness of the story. In the telling of the epic, of the narrating of ideal worlds, a community is telling itself *about itself.* In other words, epic lives within a community's sense of identity and its mythic origins. Epics also live—that is to say, they are borne out of as well as are repeated—during times of crisis and change. Louise Cowan has pointed out how the *Aeneid* and the *Exodus* are similar in these respects. They both are "telling examples of the formation of a people into a nation, depict the movement toward a destiny of fulfillment—toward a New Jerusalem or a New Troy—as the outgrowth of human and divine cooperation." [3]

Epic is the reflection upon an ideal world by a community. When this world is threatened, it rehearses itself. The repetition of the story of the Exodus each year, for example, was how Israel reminded itself of itself amidst the threat of exile and wandering. It was how it learned and relearned its identity. "Remember this day" (Exod 13:3; cf. 12:14; Deut 16:12) is the refrain of the Pentateuch. God's liberation of a people for himself (Deut 7:7–8), of his firstborn child (Exod 4:22; Hos 11:), is the atmosphere, the epic, in which all other genres of scripture—historical, legal, poetic, prophetic, apocalyptic, whatever—live and derive their meaning. It is this epic that establishes the arena of gods and humans and their interactions.

Ideal Worlds and Ideal Futures

The epic idealizes not only a sense of a collective past but also a collective future. Its concerns range from the national (*polis*) and the household (*oikos*), but also with an intervention into the troubles of the present and a movement toward culmination (*parousia*). It contains within itself both order and the troubling of order: the creation of a world, and a rage against the world that is not as it should be. The ideal world of the epic, therefore, "implies a force, an energy that impels a people forward" between these worlds. Epic is motion and striving from a mythic past to an ideal future.[4]

The Long Journey of the Self

The persistent theme of travel and journey showing up even in so many modern epics ranging from *Moby Dick* to *Lawrence of Arabia* and *Lord of the Rings* is therefore not surprising. With the modern epic—and here we generalize terribly—the journey develops on the stage of the interior in ways not readily apparent in the classical epic. The journey of the Fellowship, for example, to destroy Sauron's ring is about more than mere fantasy. It is about the fracturing of communities and loyalties to just causes. But "justice" here finds its defense and rationality within the logic of the epic itself. We shed no tears when Gandalf slays the Balrog, or when Lurtz and the countless orcs are laid low by Strider's sword. But when Boromir falls by the arrows of Lurtz, we run for the Kleenexes. We are hardly touched by the solidarity of the Nazgûl to the Witch-king of Angmar. But who is not moved by the sturdy loyalty of Samwise Gamgee to Frodo? The journey of the Fellowship sets the rest of the narrative world in motion. The journey becomes the organizing principle of the plot and how a character responds to the journey to destroy the ring reveals their identity and sense of purpose.[5]

Wisdom is the Epic Side of Truth

Walter Benjamin, one of the most significant Jewish intellectuals of the twentieth century, made the observation that "every real story" contains in some form "something useful." This something useful may consist of a "moral," or "some practical advice," a "proverb" or aphorism, but in every case the storyteller gives "counsel for [their] readers." Benjamin lamented how old-fashioned giving counsel has come to sound, and stated how in his age the sharing of experience was decaying. "In consequence we have no counsel either for ourselves or for others." It is important to understand how Benjamin understands what counsel means. It is "less an answer to a question than a proposal concerning the continuation of a story which is just unfolding." Learning to live within the continuation of a story wedded to the "fabric of real life" is what constitutes wisdom. Benjamin lamented the modern fixation on right and wrong and modernity's loss of narrative. Narrative and the telling of narrative "is reaching its end because the epic side of truth, wisdom, is dying out." [6]

Proverbs, Aphorisms, and the Continuation of Story

The calls to "the son" scattered throughout Proverbs to attend to the counsel of the father (e.g., 1:8; 3:1; 5:1; 23:26) should be read beyond the individual plain. They evoke a communal consciousness of being God's firstborn (Exod 4:22; Hos 11:1). The aphorisms in Proverbs are not directions of what to do once for all, but directorial notes on how to live within the continuation of God's epic. The repeated imagery of walking (4:12; 28:18, 26), of a path (4:25–26; 15:19), of a way (10:29; 20:24; 21:2), a highway (16:17), of discovery (16:20), and of steps (20:24) reveals that living within an epic means living on the epic side of truth—that is, living in the way of wisdom. The way of wisdom and the way of folly are contrasting forces in the ideal world created by epic.

"Whoever walks in wisdom will be delivered" (28:26), but the fool will "suddenly fall" (28:18). And whoever "trusts in their own mind is a fool" (v. 26). Trusting in oneself, collapsing oneself onto the self, leads to the slasher film of folly's destruction. But entrusting the self to the other, and walking on the way of wisdom leads to the discovery of the "good" (16:20).

Wisdom's Judgments

There is a subversive element that we have been hinting at throughout these essays on the subversive nature of the aphorism which now comes into focus when considering the aphorism as the storyteller's counsel in continuing within the narrative of the epic. That is, those who consider, meditate, and understand the aphorism demonstrate that they are on the way of wisdom. And the hasty, those who do not consider, do not meditate, do not understand, are the fools on the way to destruction. By way of illustrating this, I would like to turn to the brilliant reflections of Karl Ove Knausgaard on the pain he felt toward the poetry that never opened itself to him.

Knausgaard was at once bothered and aware of the consequences of how poems did not open for him.

> For the consequences of this were serious, much more so than merely being excluded from a literary genre. It also passed judgment on me. The poems looked into another reality, or saw reality in a different way, one that was truer than the way I knew, and the fact that it was not possible to acquire the ability to see and that it was something you either had or you didn't condemned me to a life on a lower plane, indeed, it made me one of the lowly. The pain of that insight was immense.[7]

The key portion here lies in Knausgaard's realization that the inability to penetrate the poem, or be penetrated by the poem, was a form of judgment from the poem. He knew enough to realize that the poem is the perspective of a different plane. The inability to discern this plane was a realization of one's imprisonment to a singular reality. This reality. So it is with the aphorisms of Proverbs. They are meant to shake one loose from the hegemony of this reality: the reality of the one. Folly is the inability to see wisdom as such. Pearls are not pearls to pigs. Wisdom is not wisdom to fools (cf. Matt 7:6). That is not to say that all the aphorisms of Proverbs are clear to those on the path of wisdom. Nor is it say that we cannot grow in wisdom (see, e.g., Jas 1:5). But the circular cunning of the aphorism is that if you see its message as foolish it is because you are foolish. There might be a way that seems right, but in the end it leads to death (Prov 14:12; 16:25). The appearance of rightness is the illusion that takes place on the stage of one. But wisdom, the epic side of what is right and true, does not originate from within the stage of the one—only on the stage of the two (cf. Isa 55:8–9).

The Aphorist and the Epic

The aphorisms of Proverbs, then, are the continued counsel to live within the epic of the people of God. The world is too complex, too big, and too intricate to look for the stable answers of right and wrong. To trust in one's own mind is to be convinced and content with the world as it goes; the world as it is in all its illusions. But the continued journey through the peaks and valleys of life along the rugged road of wisdom is the way that not only leads to deliverance and safety, but also the weapon with which we judge and trouble the lie-that-has-become-truth. To "trust in the Lord" is to give oneself over to the otherness of wisdom—to escape from the arid solipsism of the one and play in the wide-open spaces of the two. It is the setting down of "truth" and the pursuit of its epic-side, the other side, the way of wisdom.

EPIC-RELATED PROVERBS

Proverbs 14:15

The simple believes everything,
but the prudent gives thought to
his steps.

Where is your life based on unchecked assumptions?

Proverbs 14:23

In all toil there is profit, but mere talk tends only to poverty.

are you all talk?

Proverbs 16:19

It is better to be of a lowly spirit
with the poor than to divide the
spoil with the proud.

HOW WILL YOU PROSPER WITHOUT
BECOMING ONE OF THE PROUD?

Proverbs 16:26

A worker's appetite works for him;
his mouth urges him on.

IS YOUR HUNGER PRODUCTIVE?

Proverbs 17:24

The discerning sets his face toward
wisdom, but the eyes of a fool are
on the ends of the earth.

WHAT ARE YOU STARING AT?

A rich man's wealth is his strong city,
and like a high wall in his imagination.

Can you afford to be so deluded?

Proverbs 19:2

Desire without knowledge is not good, and whoever makes haste with his feet misses his way.

Proverbs 20:13

Love not sleep, lest you come to poverty; open your eyes, and you will have plenty of bread.

Proverbs 20:24

A man's steps are from the Lord; how then can man understand his way?

How much control do you pretend to have over your life?

The sluggard says, "There is a lion outside! I shall be killed in the streets!"

Proverbs 21:22

A wise man scales the city of
the mighty and brings down the
stronghold in which they trust.

FOR THE SAKE
OF JUSTICE,
WILL YOU
SUBVERT THE
ESTABLISHMENT?

Proverbs 21:31

The horse is made ready for the
day of battle, but the victory
belongs to the Lord.

HOW DO YOU PLAN TO WIN?

Proverbs 22:3

The prudent sees danger and
hides himself, but the simple go
on and suffer for it.

Are you looking ahead?

Proverbs 22:24-25

Make no friendship with a man given to anger,
nor go with a wrathful man, lest you learn his
ways and entangle yourself in a snare.

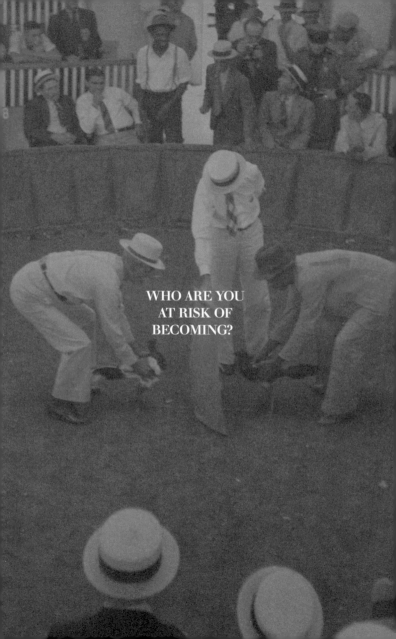

WHO ARE YOU
AT RISK OF
BECOMING?

Proverbs 22:29

Do you see a man skillful in his work? He will stand before kings; he will not stand before obscure men.

Proverbs 23:1-3

When you sit down to eat with a ruler, observe carefully what is before you, and put a knife to your throat if you are given to appetite. Do not desire his delicacies, for they are deceptive food.

HOW DO THE RICH AND POWERFUL INFLUENCE YOUR DESIRES?

221

If you faint in the day of adversity,
your strength is small.

Rescue those who are being taken away to
death; hold back those who are stumbling
to the slaughter.

What is your personal policy for dealing wth injustice?

The wicked flee when
no one pursues, but the
righteous are bold as a lion.